Ghost tricks

Horton was a small but beautiful village.
In its centre stood a very old manor house.
Nobody had lived there for many years and it had
    just been sold to a new owner.
The villagers hoped it would bec

Ann and Jess were in the same class at school.
'Today,' said Miss Murphy, 'we are all going
   to the old manor house to paint pictures of it.
   It's going to be knocked down soon and I want you
   all to have something to remember it by.'

'But they can't knock down the old house,' said Ann.
'It's been there for hundreds of years.'
'I thought they were going to make it into a museum,'
said Jess, 'so that we could see how people lived
in the olden days.'

'That was the plan,' explained Miss Murphy, 'but the
site was bought by Mr Simon Smart. He's going to
build a supermarket there.'

'Can't we do anything to stop him?' asked Ann.

'No. I'm afraid it's too late,' sighed Miss Murphy.

The class walked to the manor house.
They brought their drawing things with them.
'I've brought my camera,' said Jess, 'so I can take
  some photographs too.'
'It's stupid,' said Ann. 'Who needs another
  supermarket?'

When they had done several drawings and paintings
the girls decided to explore.
'I should be able to take some good photos here,
said Jess. 'Go and stand against the door and
I'll take one of you.'

Ann walked up to the old oak door.

'That's funny,' she said. 'It seems to be open.'

'It can't be,' said Jess.

'Yes it is,' said Ann, and she gave the door a push.

It swung open with a loud creaking sound.

The girls crept in and started to look around.
The house had looked old and shabby on the outside
but inside it looked like a palace.
'I don't understand,' gasped Ann. 'Nobody is
supposed to have lived here for years.'

'But there must be people living here now,'
    whispered Jess. 'Look! There's a fire burning in
    the fireplace and I can smell something cooking.'
'I know,' said Ann. 'It's making me feel hungry.
    I wish I had brought some sandwiches.'

The girls tip-toed down a long corridor and looked
   through an open door.
They could see a huge, old-fashioned kitchen.
There were dozens of people, all hard at work.
'What strange clothes they're wearing,' said Jess.

'Yes,' said Ann. 'Perhaps they decided to make
    this house into a museum after all.'
'It's strange that they should be cooking all that
    food,' said Jess. 'Who's going to eat it all?'
'I wish it was me,' said Ann. 'I'm starving.'

'If that is so,' said a little boy, 'you are welcome
    to join us for dinner.'
'Oh dear,' said Ann. 'We didn't know anybody was
    here. We're sorry we came into the house.'
'You are welcome,' said the boy.

'We were told that the house was going to be
    knocked down to build a supermarket,' said Ann.
    'But we're glad it's been made into a museum.'
'You don't live in here, do you?' asked Jess.

'My family has lived here for a very long time,'
    said the boy, 'but tomorrow they will pull down
    our house and we shall have nowhere to go.'
'But they can't pull it down if you live here,'
    said Ann.
'Yes they can,' said the boy sadly.

14

'All my family are here,' he said. 'We have been here for hundreds of years but tomorrow we must go. Tonight we are having our farewell feast.'

'Is that why you're wearing fancy-dress?' asked Ann.

'No!' laughed the boy. 'That's because I'm a ghost.'

'Wow!' gasped Ann. 'I've never seen a ghost before.'
'Are you going to haunt us?' asked Jess nervously.
'Of course not,' said the boy. 'We're not interested
in haunting people. You mustn't believe silly ghost
stories. Come and meet my family.'

The boy introduced Ann and Jess to the other
    members of his family.
There seemed to be crowds of them.
They were all very sad that their house was
    going to be pulled down.

'What a pity we didn't meet you earlier,' said the
boy's mother. 'It's such a shame that this must
be your first and last visit. We all love meeting
new people. I'm sure I shall never
settle down in a supermarket.'

'Perhaps you won't have to move,' said Jess. 'I've
    got a plan. If it works, you'll be able to go on
    living here and hundreds of people will want
    to visit you.'
'What sort of plan?' asked the boy.
'This is what you must do...,' said Jess.

Next morning, Mr Simon Smart and his workmen
  came to knock down the house.
Ann and Jess were waiting for them on the doorstep.
'You can't come in here,' they said.
'Go away!' snapped Mr Smart. 'This is my land now.'

'You can't knock down this house,' said Ann. 'We think it should be turned into a museum.'
'That's too bad,' said Mr Smart. 'I'm going to build a smart new Smart's supermarket on this site.'
'You can't,' said Jess. 'There are people inside.'

'What!' snapped Mr Smart. 'I'll soon get them out.'
He pushed past the girls and went through the door.
'The plan's working,' thought the girls and they
   followed him into the house.
'You can't fool me,' said Mr Smart, 'there's
   no one here.'

'We are here,' whispered a ghostly voice.

'Who said that?' said Mr Smart nervously. 'Is this
  some sort of joke?'

'We are all here,' said several ghostly voices.

They seemed to be coming from all over the house.

Mr Smart began to back towards the door.

He felt a tap on his shoulder.

'I'm here too,' said a floating ghost.

Mr Smart's mouth fell open and his eyes grew wide.

There were ghosts everywhere.

'Help!' wailed Mr Smart. 'Get me out of here.'

At that moment, the door slammed shut.

'You can go when you've promised not to knock down
    the house,' said Ann.

'Never, never, never!' shouted Mr Smart.

Mr Smart dashed towards the door.
The little boy opened it for him.
Mr Smart couldn't believe what was happening.
His workmen were floating in the air.
'Get us down! Get us down!' they shouted.

The workmen's spades were floating, too.

So were their diggers and concrete-mixers.

'Now will you promise not to knock down this house?'
  said Jess.

'Anything! I'll promise anything!' gasped Mr Smart.
'Just let us go and I will never come near this
horrible place again.'
The workmen and their tools floated gently down
to the ground.

Mr Smart and his workmen ran away.
'I don't think they'll come back,' said Jess.
All the ghosts began to cheer.
'It worked! It worked!' shouted Ann.
'I knew it would,' said Jess.

That night the old house came to life.
The ghosts had the best party of all time.
Ann and Jess were the guests of honour.
They found some of the games rather difficult.
It's not easy playing Hide-and-Seek with a
    family of ghosts.

The best one of all was musical chairs, in mid-air.
It was fun floating through the air.
The chairs went up and down and round and
 round, in time to the music.
When the music stopped, the children were
 quite dizzy.

The old house was turned into a museum.

The villagers were pleased.

Miss Murphy took her class to see how people had
    lived hundreds of years ago.

But only Jess and Ann saw the Ghosts.